Silly Dog

Chester Dowens

Silly Dog

By

Eddie Bowman

Illustrated by

Howard Prater

Ozark Publishing, Inc.
P.O. Box 228
Prairie Grove, AR 72753

Dedicated to my grandson Dustin Wayne Burk

Library of Congress cataloging-in-publication data

Bowman, Eddie, 1939-
    Silly dog / by Eddie Bowman ; illustrated by Howard Prater.
        p.   cm.
    Summary: A funny-looking stray dog finds a home with people who appreciate it's silliness.
    ISBN 1-56763-324-2 (cloth). -- ISBN 1-56763-325-0 (pbk.)
    [1. Dogs--Fiction.   2. Stories in rhyme.]   I. Prater, Howard, ill. II. Title.
    PZ8.3.B6775Si   1998
    [E]--dc21

                                       96-540-14
                                          CIP
                                          AC

Printed in the United States of America

I fell in love with a silly dog,

A big round furry bundle.

He had big feet like a green bullfrog

And a face like . . . a monkey in the jungle.

Well, I called him Fred
And I called him George
And then I called him Billy.

But he wouldn't do a thing
Till I got the right name
When I finally called him Silly.

"Here, Silly!
Hey, Silly!
Come here, Silly Dog!

Rub your nose against my face.

Wag your tail all over the place.

Chase me down and chew on
my shoelace. Here, Silly Dog."

I fell in the mud
One day at school.
I looked like a real hillbilly.

I called my mom
And I played it cool.
I said, "Please bring old Silly!"

Well, he licked my clothes

And he licked my nose

And he made me look real dilly.

When the teacher asked how I got so clean . . .

I told her, "It was Silly!"

     As a boy growing up on a hillside farm in southwest Missouri near Purdy, Eddie spent much of his time clearing new ground and raising strawberries. His parents taught him to be honest, work hard and treat people with respect. His interests include motivational speaking, inspirational teaching, and entertaining. For several years he has been a comedian on the Brumley music show in Branson, Missouri. He is also a song writer, musician and writer of inspirational and children's books.

     Eddie and his wife, Evelyn, have four children and four grandchildren.

     Eddie loves to tell stories of humor and common sense with practical applications for everyday life. He brings laughter and encouragement to readers and audiences of all ages.